The
Mary Ann

Keith Gaines

Mr Belter was talking to the class at Waterloo School.
'You know that for the last two weeks we have
been working on our project about trees.
Well, next Thursday we are going on a trip.
We are going to look closely at lots of trees.
It's not far away, but it will take us just
under an hour to get there.
How do you think we are going to get there?'

The children put up their hands.
'Are we going by bus?' said Jamila.
'No,' said Mr Belter. 'Not by bus.'
'Are we going by train?' said Rocky.
'No,' said Mr Belter. 'Not by train.'
'Are we going by car?' said Kevin.
'No,' said Mr Belter. 'Not by car.'

3

'Are we going to walk there?' said Ben.
'Well,' said Mr Belter.
'We are going to walk some of the way,
and we'll be walking when we get there,
but we are not walking all the way there.
'Are we flying there?' said Tony.
All the children laughed.

'No, we're not flying,' said Mr Belter.
'I'm afraid we haven't got enough
money to use planes for school trips.
There's something that no-one has thought of yet.'
'Are we going in a boat?' said Rocky.
'Yes,' said Mr Belter. 'We are going in a boat.'
'Like a ferry boat?' said Jamila.
'No,' said Mr Belter. 'Not as big as a ferry boat.
We are going on a narrow-boat, along the canal!'

5

'Have any of you ever been on a narrow-boat?'
asked Mr Belter.
Kevin put up his hand.
'I have, Mr Belter,' he said.
Kevin remembered the day that the school football
team had been playing away against Ripton Rovers.
The referee had told the two teams that he didn't want
to see any rough play or any fouls.
First Kevin had pushed one of the Ripton players and
the referee had put Kevin's name in his little red book.
Then Kevin had knocked another player over.
After this foul, the referee had sent Kevin off.
Kevin had walked off the pitch and he had kept
on walking until he came to the canal and
saw a narrow-boat.
No-one was on the boat, and Kevin had gone inside it.
He had fallen asleep on the boat,
and the boat's owners had come back.
They hadn't noticed Kevin, but when he woke up and
got off the boat, the boat had moved and he was lost!

'Would you like to tell us all about the
narrow-boat, Kevin?' said Mr Belter.
Suddenly Kevin thought,
'It sounds as if Mr Belter has forgotten about
when I went on the boat and got lost.
I got into trouble then, and I might get into more
trouble if I tell him about it again.'
'Come on, Kevin,' said Mr Belter.
'Tell us about when you've been on a narrow-boat.'
'Er...er...' said Kevin. 'Oh! did you say *been*?
I thought you said *seen*!
I've seen a narrow-boat in one of my car books.'
Mr Belter shook his head.

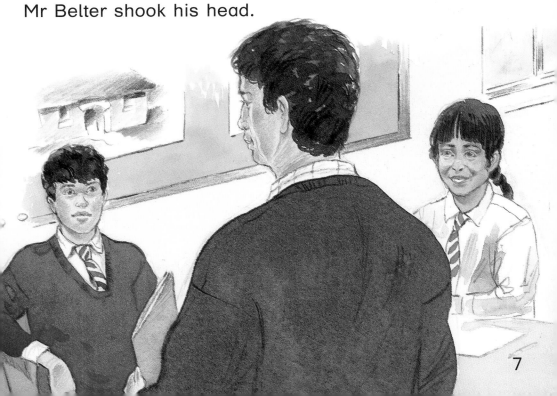

'We will be away all day, so you will all have to
bring something to eat and something to drink,'
said Mr Belter.
'You should come in your school clothes
but just for this trip, you can come in jeans.
Everyone must bring a coat, because we might
have rain.
Here is a letter about the trip.'
Mr Belter gave a pile of papers to Tessa.
'Tessa,' said Mr Belter.
'Go round the class and give one letter to each
girl and boy.
Take this letter home and get your Mum or your
Dad to sign the bit at the end to say you can
go on the trip.
Cut off that bit and bring it back to me.
I want it back tomorrow. When do I want it back,
Kevin?'

'Tomorrow, Mr Belter,' said Kevin.

'Yes, that's right,' said Mr Belter.

'Now, is everything clear to everyone?'

Rocky put up his hand.

'Yes, Rocky?' said Mr Belter. 'What is it?'

'How much do we have to pay to go on the trip?' asked Rocky.

'Ah!' said Mr Belter.

'I'm pleased to say that this trip is part of your project. It's in school time and you don't have to pay anything.'

A week later, on Thursday morning, all the children waited in the classroom.

Mrs Jones and Mr Belter came in.

'School trips are such fun,' Mrs Jones said to Mr Belter.

'I can talk to the children and
I can get to know them much better.
I do like to keep a close eye on all
the children in the school.'

'That's good,' said Mr Belter.

'Because one of us should try to keep
a close eye on Kevin.
I don't think I've ever been on a trip when
I didn't lose a kid – and it was usually Kevin!'

'Right, class,' said Mr Belter.
'In a minute I want you all to line up outside.
Mrs Jones will go at the front and I will go at the back.
We are going to walk to the part of the
canal which is near Wellington Square.'
'It's not near at all!' said Kevin. 'It's miles away!'
'It's not that far,' said Mr Belter.
'It will only take us about fifteen minutes.
When we get there, I will give you a paper to work on.
There will be six things for you to do or to find out.
The boat will take us to where we
are going to look at trees.
We will be on the boat for about fifty minutes.
When we get off the boat, we can eat our food.
Then you can all go and look for things in the trees.
We will have about an hour and forty minutes there.
Then I will blow my whistle.
When you hear my whistle, come back to the boat.
You should be able to leave school at the same time as
you usually do. Right! Let's get going!'

The children all lined up outside.
'We are all ready, Mrs Jones,' shouted Mr Belter.
'Come along, children,' said Mrs Jones.
'We'll go this way round the Square,
then we can look at the shops as we go by.'

Mrs Jones, the children and Mr Belter
walked round Wellington Square.
Mrs Jones took the children by the shops.
They went by Jamila's shop.
They went by Rocky's house.
They went by Wing Chan's take-away.
'Keep together,' shouted Mr Belter.
They walked by Mr Keeping's house and
by Mrs Valentine's house.
They passed the house where Tony and Tessa live.

'Go left when you get to the house where
the doctor lives,' shouted Mr Belter.
'Which one is that?' said Mrs Jones.
'It's Number 21,' said Jamila.
'It's the house on the corner.'
As they turned the corner, Mr Belter shouted,
'Now just keep walking until you reach the canal.'

'There it is,' said Tony. 'There's the canal.'
'It's miles away,' said Kevin.
'Why couldn't we have gone on a bus?'
'Because I want you to look at some special trees and you can't get to them on a bus,' said Mr Belter.
'If you were not going on the narrow-boat,
you really would have to walk for miles and miles.
Anyway, you'll like sitting on the canal boat.'
'I get sea-sick,' said Kevin.
'Don't worry, Kevin,' said Mr Belter.
'No-one gets canal-sick.'

14

When they got to the canal,
the boat was waiting for them.
Kevin looked at the boat.
The boat was tied up, close to the bank of the canal.
Kevin saw that the boat was called the *Mary Ann*.
'Oh, no!' thought Kevin. 'This is the same boat that I
went on when we played Ripton Rovers and
I got sent off.
Still, I don't need to worry.
The people on the boat never saw me.'

The teachers were talking to a man and a lady.
'This is Jack,' said Mr Belter to Mrs Jones.
'And this is Peg. They own this narrow-boat.'
'How do you do?' said Mrs Jones.

'Now,' said Mr Belter.
'I want all you children to come and
get a paper from me.
Then I want you, one at a time, to step onto the deck,
go down the steps and sit in the cabin.'
Jack and Peg helped the children to get on the boat.
When they were all on the boat, Jack untied the
boat and Peg started the engine.
'Look at your papers,' said Mr Belter.
'There are six things for you to do.'

The children looked at their papers, which said:

Waterloo School Canal Trip

1 Find out the name of the boat.

2 Put in each missing bit of this picture of the boat.

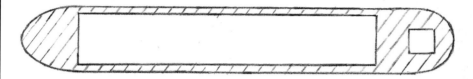

3 Find three different leaves.

4 Pick a tree and draw it.

5 Draw the barks of two different trees.

6 Draw three animals that live in or near the trees.
(An animal can be anything living and moving.)

'I thought we were coming for a trip,' said Tessa.
'I didn't think we would be doing all this work.'
'I don't think this is work,' said Jamila.
'This is just the sort of thing I like doing.'
'What's this boat's name?' said Rocky.
'I didn't look before we got on.'
'That's easy,' said Kevin. 'I can tell you that!
It's the *Mary Ann*.'
'How do we know what to put on this bit of the
picture of the boat?' asked Ben.
'We can't see this part –
it's behind the curtains back there.'
'We will have to find out from one of the
people who own the boat,' said Rocky.
'No, you won't,' said Kevin. 'There's a table and a bed.'
'How do you know that, Kevin?' asked Mr Belter.
'Er…er…Well, I…er…that is, I…er…well,
the people live on this boat, don't they?
They eat and sleep, but there isn't a table or
a bed in here, so there must be a table and
a bed behind those curtains!'
'How very clever of you to work that out, Kevin,'
said Mr Belter. 'Well done!'

19

'Here we are,' said Jack, as he
brought the boat to a stop.
There were lots of trees all around them.
Jack looked at his watch.
'It took us forty-eight minutes,' he said.
'We made good time.'
Everyone got off the boat.
'Right,' shouted Mr Belter.
'You can eat your food now.'

Fifteen minutes later, Kevin was still eating.
'All the other children have finished,' said Mrs Jones.
'And you are still eating.'
'I've nearly finished,' said Kevin.
'I've just got two more sausage rolls and
a pork pie to eat.
My Mum says that big lads like me
have to eat a lot so they get bigger and stronger.'

'Right!' shouted Mr Belter. 'Everyone listen.
For the next hour or two you are going to
look at these lovely trees.
Look at your papers.
I think you have already done the
two things about the canal narrow-boat.
You will have four more things to do.
They will take you quite a long time, so
don't spend too much time on one thing.
You can't get lost.
There's a fence all round these trees, so
you can't go too far away.'

Mr Belter held up a whistle.
'When you hear this whistle, start to walk back here.
It sounds like this.'
Mr Belter blew the whistle.
It was very loud.
'I will carry on until everyone is back here,'
said Mr Belter,
'so just keep walking towards the sound of the whistle.
Try and do as many of the things on your paper as
you can.
I want to see if anyone can do *all* the things on the
paper.'

Will anyone do all six things on the paper?
Who do you think will do all six things on the paper?

If you think it'll be Rocky, go to p 24.
If you think it'll be Ben, go to p 26.
If you think it'll be Jamila, go to p 27.
If you think it'll be Tony, go to p 28.
If you think it'll be Tessa, go to p 28.
If you think it'll be Kevin, go to p 30.
If you think it'll be Wing Chan, go to p 31.

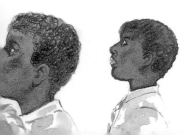

Rocky had already done the first two things.
'Let's see,' he thought.
'I have to find three different leaves.'
Rocky walked through the trees.
'There's one sort,' he thought as he picked one up.
'And there's a really big one…
and there's a much smaller one – that makes three!'
Rocky looked up into the trees.
'Ah,' he thought. 'There's an animal – I'll put that down.
Now, what have I got to do next?'

Go to p 25.

Rocky looked at his paper.
'I have to pick a tree and draw it,' he thought.
Rocky looked around.
'That's a good tree to draw,' he thought.
'I will draw that tree and I will draw the
shadow of the tree under it.
That will make a really good picture.'

An hour and a half later, Rocky was still
working on his tree picture when
Mr Belter blew his whistle.
When Rocky got back, Mr Belter asked him if
he had done all six things.
'No,' said Rocky.
'I did not draw the bark and
I did not find three animals.
I spent too much time on my picture of a tree.'

Rocky did not do all six things in time.
See if you can find out who did!
Go back to p 23 and try again!

Ben had already done the first two things and
it did not take him long to find three different leaves.
'I hope I'll win,' he thought.
He picked a small tree, which did not take long to draw.
Then he did two pictures of the bark of two trees.
As he was looking at the bark, he saw a big
beetle, climbing up the tree.
'That's one sort of animal,' thought Ben.
Ben saw birds in the trees.
'That's another sort of animal,' he thought.
Now, what can I find for the last animal?'

Go on to p 32.

Jamila had already done the first two things and
it did not take her long to find three different leaves.
Then she picked a small tree.
It did not take her long to draw it.
Then she did two pictures of the bark of two trees.
'Now,' thought Jamila.
'I have to find three animals that live in or near the trees.'
Jamila looked around. Jamila listened.
There was a little noise behind her.
'Something's moving about in the leaves,' she thought.
Very quietly, she turned round. There was a hedgehog.
She followed the hedgehog.

She was still watching when Mr Belter blew his whistle.
When she got back, Mr Belter asked if she had finished.
'No,' said Jamila. 'I was watching a hedgehog.
I only found one animal.'

Jamila did not do all six things in time.
See if you can find out who did!
Go back to p 23 and try again!

Tony and Tessa ran through the trees.
'Hey, Tessa,' said Tony.
'We could play a great game in these trees!
There's lots of time to do this work.'
'Yes,' said Tessa.
'You could be one of the aliens with a ray gun.
I have to get you with my bombs!'
'OK!' said Tony. 'I'll give you one minute to
get away, then I'll come after you.'
'I bet you can't catch me!' shouted Tessa,
as she ran off.
Tony waited a minute, then he started chasing
after Tessa.
'Fizz! Pow!' shouted Tony, as he chased Tessa all
round the trees, but after a while he lost her.

Go to p 29.

Tessa ran through the trees.
When she came to a very big tree, she had a good idea.
She climbed up into the tree, pulling herself
up into the branches.
Then she hid on a branch and waited for Tony.
'Where can she be?' thought Tony.
'I'm sure she'll be somewhere round here.'
Suddenly – Splat!
Tessa dropped a banana on Tony's head.
'I've won,' said Tessa.
'I got you with my banana bomb.'

Suddenly, from a long way away
came the noise of Mr Belter's whistle.
'Oh, no!' said the twins.
'We'll have to race back and we haven't done our work!'

Tony did not do all six things in time and
Tessa did not do all six things in time.
See if you can find out who did!

Go back to p 23 and try again!

'Well, I've done the first two things,' thought Kevin.
'There's lots of time to do the rest.
I feel a bit tired after all that walking this morning.
I think I'll have a rest behind this tree for a while.'
Kevin sat behind the tree. Soon he was asleep.

He was woken up by the sound of Mr Belter's whistle.
He had not gone far and he was the first to get back.
'That was quick,' said Mr Belter.
'Have you done them all?'
'Er…not quite,' said Kevin.

Kevin did not do all six things in time.
See if you can find out who did!
Go back to p 23 and try again!

Wing Chan liked trees.
He had a book all about trees and
he had brought his book with him.
Wing Chan looked at the trees around him.
He looked at the trees in his book.
He soon found three different leaves, but
he knew that there were lots of different leaves.
'I will find as many different leaves as I can,'
he thought.
'There is lots of time to do this other work.'

Wing Chan had found fifteen different leaves when
Mr Belter blew his whistle.
'Oh, no!' thought Wing Chan, as he raced back.
'I have not finished all my work!'

Wing Chan did not do all six things in time.
See if you can find out who did!
Go back to p 23 and try again!

Ben sat down on the ground and
leaned back against a tree.
He looked at the ground.
There were lots of dead leaves under the tree.
As he looked more closely, he saw that there were
snails moving in the leaves.
'That's another animal,' thought Ben.

Just as he put it down on his paper,
Mr Belter blew his whistle.
Ben raced back to Mr Belter.
'Have you finished, Ben?' asked Mr Belter.
'Yes,' said Ben.
'Well done, Ben!' said Mr Belter.
'You are the only one who has finished!
You have done all six things on the paper!'

The end